Molly Bang

TEN, NINE, EIGHT

SCHOLASTIC INC.
New York Toronto London Auckland Sydney

ISBN 0-590-45583-4

All rights reserved. Published by Scholastic Inc.,
730 Broadway, New York, NY 10003, by arrangement with
William Morrow & Company, Inc.

12 11 10 9 8 7 6 5 4   3 4 5 6/9

Printed in the U.S.A.   08

FOR DEBORAH,
PRESHIEL, SYLVIA, VIKI
AND THEIR CHILDREN
AND FOR
DICK AND MONIKA,
WITH THANKS
AND
LOVE

10 small toes all washed and warm

9 soft friends
in a quiet room

 **8** square windowpanes
with falling snow

**7** empty shoes in a short straight row

6 pale seashells
hanging down

5 round buttons on a yellow gown

4 sleepy eyes which open and close

3 loving kisses on cheeks and nose

2 strong arms around a fuzzy bear's head

1 big girl all ready
for bed